I Know A Farm

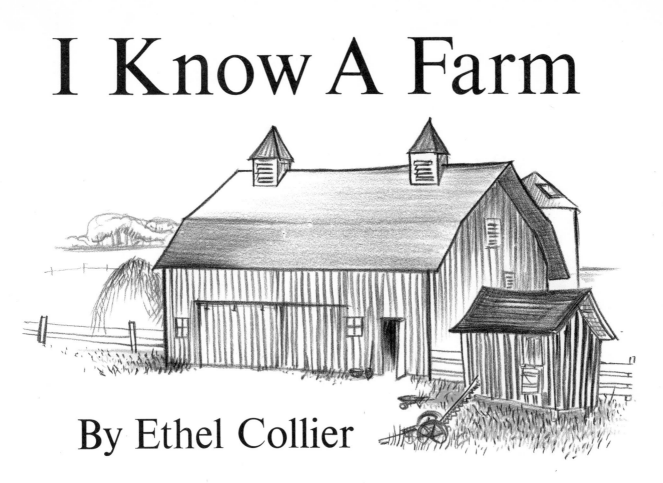

By Ethel Collier

Illustrated By Honoré Guilbeau

Young Scott Books

I know a farm.

One time I went to it with my father.

On the way to the farm, I saw
a little green hill.

I told my father, "I wish we had time
to roll down that little green hill."

My father said, "We can stop the car.
Then you can roll down the little green hill."

So I did.

Then, on the way to the farm,
we went over some water.

In the water I saw a big fish.

I told my father, "I wish
we had time to get that fish."

My father said, "We can stop the car.
See if you can get a fish."

I went to the water.

I had to hold my hand in it a long time.

Once a little fish came near my hand!
But I did not get him.

My father made a paper boat for the water.

The water took it into some woods.

I said, "I wish I could go into the woods with the boat."

But my father said, "We do not have time."

So I did not get into any woods.

Then we came to the farm. It was the farm
of Mr. and Mrs. Green.

First of all, Mrs. Green gave me an apple.

Mr. Green said, "What would you like to see on this farm?"

I said, "I never saw what is in a barn."

The farmer and my father took me to the barn.

It was big and gray.
It had big doors.
They were not open.

A little door was open.

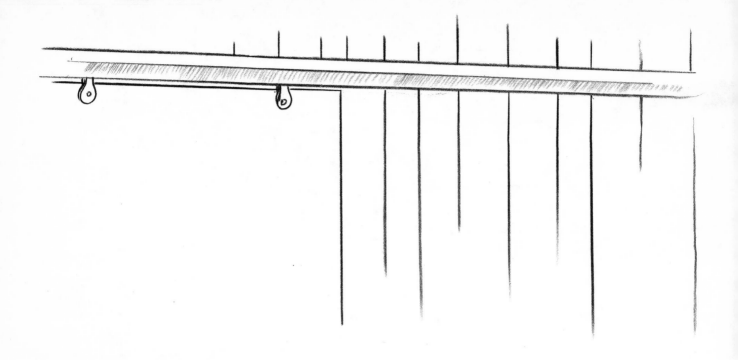

Mr. Green said, "See what you can find in the barn!"

I went in.

In the barn, just a little sun came in.

At first I could not see much.
I did not see or hear any animals.
But there was a good smell.

I could tell that there were animals
in that barn!

Then a mouse ran by.

I know it was a mouse. I have a picture of a mouse.

She had some hay and she ran into a little room.

I could hear something.

It came from the room
that the mouse ran into.

The door was open a little.
I went to see what was there.

A horse was there. He was big
and black. His back was round.
He had a long black tail.

I think the horse could hear me.
I could see him turn his head.

He had a long face.

But I liked the way his eyes were.
So I went into the room.

The horse put his head down.
I put my hand to his face.
I could tell that he wanted my apple.

All at once he took my apple and ate it!

I went back to the big room of the barn.
Way up near the top I could see some hay.
I could climb up to it.

The hay had a good smell.
There was a big hill of it.
I could jump in the hay.

And I did.

When I did, I saw a hen fly up.
She gave the hen call, "Cut, cut, cut!"

The hen would fly a little.
Then she would jump a little.
That was the way she got down from the hay.

I found the nest the hen came from.
It was a round nest in the hay.
It was just as big as the hen.
An egg was in it!
The egg was warm.
I think the hen had just put it there.

I took the egg to give it
to the farmer.

Then I could hear something little
in the hay.
I found where it came from.

It was kittens!
It was four kittens in a nest in the hay.

The kittens were gray and black.
Their ears and tails were too little.
But I could tell that they were kittens.
I took a gray one to hold.

Then a big cat came up into the hay
with a jump.
She did not want me there. I could tell that.
I put her kitten back into the nest.

She got into the nest and I went back a little way.

But then I could not see the kittens.

For a long time I sat in the hay
away from the kittens.

I saw a little bird fly into the barn.

He came in like a jet.

He went to the top of the barn.
Way up there, I could see another nest.
The bird went into it.

Then I could hear my father call me.

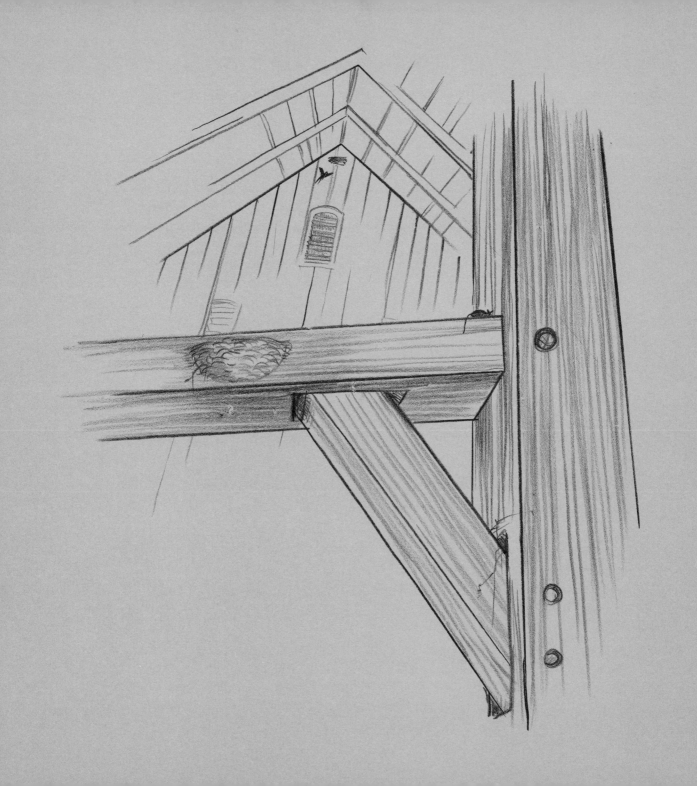

I had to hold the hen egg in one hand
and climb down from the hay.

In the big room, I saw the mouse.
I know she had a nest
with some mouse children in it.

All the little barn animals had nests.
But I could not find the mouse nest.
And I could hear my father call me again.

On the way back to the farm house, I saw
a little hen house. Hens were in it.
I could not see them but I could hear,
"Cut, cut, cut!"

There was not time to go in.

I went to the farm house. At the back door
there was a good smell.
It was cake.

I told how the horse took my apple.
Mrs. Green said, "Would you like some apple cake?"

I said, "Yes, thank you,"
and she cut some apple cake for me.

I put my hen egg down.

I sat by some flowers and ate the cake.
It was warm.

I told how I found the egg
and how the bird came in like a jet.
I told about the kittens.

Then we had to go home.
I gave the hen egg to the farmer.

He said, "Keep the hen egg."

I said, "Thank you. I would like
some kittens, too, please."

But Mr. Green said that the kittens
were too little. They had to stay
with the big cat.

Then Mrs. Green cut some flowers.
They were for me.

I said, "Thank you for the good time
on the farm."

They said, "Come back and see us again."

They wanted me to come back!

My father and I got into the car.

And then what do you think Mrs. Green said?

She told me, "Come back when the kittens are not so little. Then you may take one home with you to keep!"

DATE DUE

PRINTED IN U.S.A.

170 IDEAL